Registration

Please compl~~ete~~ your
Preschool Bo~~ok~~ ~~t~~eacher.

Child's name. _____

Sex: _____

Address: _____

_____

Please return
KELTY ♡
_____

_____

_____

- 6

~~d~~etails may be used for evaluation of
~~i~~f you do NOT want to participate in the
~~ple~~ase tick the box. ☐

~~Informatio~~n update

~~Please updat~~e these details if you change address
~~and return this f~~orm to your nursery teacher.

_____

_____

~~Addr~~ess: _____

_____

~~Name~~s: _____

_____

~~Date of b~~irth: ___ _____ ___

New nursery
(if changed): ___ ___

play@home

Nursery age children play to enjoy themselves, not for the good it is doing them. All play involves movement which can be health and exercise related.

Exercise is the first step towards joining in with sport.

This book introduces play activities and ideas which are appropriate to children's stages of development. This means they enjoy them, and at the same time learn different skills involving thinking, moving, communicating, socialising and imitating.

This not only forms the basis of good physical development but provides the necessary foundation for all learning. Balance, control, agility, coordination of eye, brain and muscles, combined with being able to handle materials correctly, and having good body control can lead to feelings of confidence and self-worth. These are the keys to learning and will give children a better start in reading, writing and counting.

Fair play

It is never too early to teach your children about playing fair. Take advantage of opportunities at home to encourage respect for other family members; to learn to share toys; to be nice and patient; and to take turns.

In other words praise your child for fair play.

Praising effort is important, particularly when young children are still developing skills such as running, jumping and coordination. Success should be based on joining in and trying, rather than 'being the best' as only one person can be the best.

Let's encourage fair play with our children. Being a good role model is important, whether you are actively involved in the game or just watching. If you are polite and respectful, both 'on the field and off the field', your child is more likely to develop the same attitudes.

Mentioning the words fair play as often as possible will help your child to understand what it means from this early stage.

LEEP Recycling Ltd.
0131 538 5381
www.leep.org.uk

Bookbug

Bookbug encourages parents and children to read together from birth. We work in partnership with the NHS and every local authority through the library service or education department, to gift four free bags of books to every baby, toddler, 3- and 5-year-old in Scotland.

If you haven't received your free Bookbug Explorer Bag for your 3-year-old, please ask at your nursery for more details.

Reading and health

Early book-sharing promotes attachment, speech and language development and infant mental health. Rhythm and rhyme are the building blocks of language, so singing supports talking and, later on, reading. Getting to know songs and rhymes can make you feel good and build confidence for parents, carers and children.

Bookbug Sessions take place at your local library or community group. These are free, fun, story, song and rhyme sessions for 0-4-year-olds. Find details of your local Bookbug Session at **www.scottishbooktrust.com/localbookbugsessions**

Bookbug is run by Scottish Book Trust and funded by the Scottish Government and Creative Scotland.

To find out more visit **www.scottishbooktrust.com/bookbug**

Contents

Introduction

It is good for children and adults to play together. Equal partners in play means equally valuing what each other does and children are more likely to respond to adults they respect and trust.

This book promotes parents and carers as children's first and most important teachers. It promotes their role in developing and reinforcing daily exercise through play. It gives parents and children ideas for play which can be further developed through imaginative and creative thinking. This book familiarises children with many of the activities presented by playgroup leaders, nursery teachers or primary school teachers, resulting in enhanced learning and a more confident child.

The play@home preschool programme continues on from play@home baby and play@home toddler, starting babies and toddlers along the pathway of health, exercise and learning from day one.

If your preschooler has missed play@home baby and play@home toddler, he or she can still begin with play@home preschool. It is never too late to start.

Note:
For ease of reading and not to show any preference, we use both his and her throughout the programme. For children with special needs, some of these activities may need to be adapted. Discuss this with your child's therapist.

The importance of play@home

The first seven years of life are the most influential in establishing good exercise habits and setting the foundation for learning throughout life. Everything children do is exercise related, whether it is talking (exercising the jaw and brain) or walking. Having daily exercise routines at an early age helps children to become strong and healthy as they grow. This develops their self esteem and encourages them to 'have a go' at new activities.

It is important for parents and carers to be active with their children, not only as role models, but also for their own health and energy. This provides the foundation for a physically active life for the whole family, and encourages enjoyment of physical activities, sport and exercise.

Benefits of the programme

This book:

- Encourages you to establish daily health-related routines with your child.

- Encourages you as parents and carers to become your children's first teachers.

- Encourages your child's enjoyment of physical activity which will lead to a healthier life.

- Develops body awareness and promotes the development of good patterns of movement.

- Promotes the value of finding playmates for your child, so that they learn to interact socially and think about others.

- Encourages communication through talking and listening.

- Stimulates your child's curiosity, imagination, and creativity.

- Promotes the value of giving praise and positive reassurance.

- Encourages good loving touch in your family and strengthens parent/child relationships.

- Promotes the value of you, the parent, doing daily exercise as a role model for your child.

- Familiarises your child with activities presented at nurseries and primary schools.

How to use your programme

- Begin by reading the section 'Facts about children' (page 8) and then read the 'Child safety' section (page 12).

- Read about massage for children. Massage can be used at any time to soothe, relax, reduce stress and to help strengthen your relationship with your child.

- Set aside time each day to organise an activity for your child. You will find more energetic activities at the beginning of this section and quieter play towards the end of it.

- Choose activities you think your child will like, and that suit your family situation. Remember all children are different and have their own timetable of development. Most activities can be made more or less difficult depending on what your child can do.

- Play only for as long as it is, enjoyable. This will be 15 minutes or less for most activities, and you can always go back to them at another time.

- Vary the activities to allow your child time to play alone, to play with you, and to play with other children of the same age.

- Use the pages 112 to 127 for ideas on how to use your play@home activities when organising play for groups of children, for example, at a birthday party.

- Use the ideas in this book as starting points for your own ideas. Make your own games, invent your own toys. Share your ideas and discoveries with others.

Facts about children

Development

Your child never stops developing. The order of development is the same in all children, but the rate of development varies from stage to stage and from child to child. It does not happen overnight.

Preschoolers tend to be more cooperative than toddlers, are able to do more for themselves, are eager to please you and seem easier to live with. They have a better understanding of what the consequences of their actions will be, for example, they know throwing a ball over the fence means it will no longer be there to play with. The preschooler thinks about how something works and makes it work.

Preschoolers have confidence in their abilities and want to be more independent, although they need to know their parents or carers are always there to come back to. They are adventurous, will climb trees and playground equipment and can usually run quite fast. They develop the ability to hop, jump and go up and down stairs with one foot on each step. They learn to throw and catch a ball quite well, make a good attempt at dressing themselves, can use a knife and fork and develop better control of hand activities (like using a pencil). They will swap between using their left and right hands and feet, to do different activities and need to be allowed to do this.

It is in the preschool years that children begin to become aware of the role of each person in the family and will begin to copy parts of each person's behaviour.

If parents and carers are active in teaching (by demonstrating and joining in with play activities) their children will be actively learning; play is their 'work'.

Play

Play and play materials have educational value, and are part of the basic needs of all children to assist them in their stages of development. Play also stops them feeling bored, which can lead to frustration and bad temper. Provide children with interesting play activities appropriate to their individual stages of development, remembering that toys which interest one child may not interest another.

Play helps children to discover, to practise old skills and develop new skills, to concentrate, to experiment, to use their imagination and to develop physically. It gives them emotional satisfaction and a sense of achievement. Play is the basis of their learning and should be fun.

Social interaction

During the preschool years children need to learn to interact and play cooperatively with each other. They need to learn to share and to take turns, and to develop behaviour that is acceptable in the world outside the family. They begin to use and understand language and instructions which help them to express themselves and understand other people's needs. Parents and carers can help children to develop tools to help them solve their own problems. It is important they understand the need to argue with words rather than their fists or other weapons.

Competition

Children play for the fun of it and are not usually interested in winning or losing. The idea of competition and winning is usually introduced to them by adults. Some competition is healthy because it encourages children, as individuals, to try to do their best and to do better. This competition should be directed at personal improvement rather than competing against others. The role of parents and carers involves encouraging their children to do their best when participating, and to enjoy their activities, rather than to promote their own values of winning to their children. After a game or competition the question to children should be 'did you have fun?' rather than 'did you win?'. They respond well to praise and positive reassurance for all their efforts.

Books

Books are important in developing the communication skills of listening, thinking, understanding and speaking. Reading books with your children helps to develop their visual understanding and ability to notice detail, and stimulate the imagination. An early enjoyment of books provides a foundation for a child's more formal education later on. Young children should not be forced to look at books when they would clearly prefer to be doing something else, but by seeing adults enjoy and care for books, they learn by example. Books, magazines, newspapers, comics should all be seen around the home as valued and looked after. Young children should be encouraged to copy adults even before they can read.

Nutrition

Children need good food and regular small snacks because they are very active and growing fast. Eating habits vary enormously from one child to another – some eat like birds and others have ravenous appetites. It is important to provide them with healthy foods containing all the nutrients they need, so they begin to learn good eating habits at home. A variety of fruit should be eaten at snack time. For information about healthy meals and snacks for children and the whole family contact your health visitor.

Note:
If you feel that your child is not progressing as expected and you think there may be something wrong, contact your health visitor or doctor.

Child safety

This is a time when your child is becoming increasingly independent from you and your home. Begin to give simple explanations of safety precautions, as you make your home safe for your child.

Car safety

Make sure your child is always buckled into the correctly sized car seat.

You need to look for the next stage of child car seat at around 4 years of age when your child becomes too big for the smaller car seat. If you buy a booster and harness make sure they are 'Standards' approved. Always use them.

Falls

Your child is more adventurous now. Play equipment needs to be correctly designed and maintained and the ground surface made of impact absorbing material such as rubber matting or bark. Secure window safety catches on upper floor windows.

Burns

At this age you can teach your child to recognise the hot and cold taps by colour and to only turn on the cold tap. Make sure your hot water temperature is no more than 55°C. Apply cold water for ten minutes to any burns.

Dress your child in close fitting nightwear. Put a fireguard in front of your fire.

Poisoning

Your child is attracted to the contents of bottles and containers during play. Many pills look like sweets. Never call medication 'sweets' or 'lollies'. Ask your chemist to fit child resistant lids on all your medicine bottles.

Keep medicines and household cleaners in a high locked cupboard. Garden poisons must be locked away. Never store poisonous liquids in soft drink containers. If your child has been poisoned give water or milk to drink and then seek medical advice – phone the accident and emergency department or your doctor.

Water safety

Supervise your child at all times when near water. Flotation aids do not remove the need for constant supervision.

Safety checklist

- ☑ Use an approved child car seat on all journeys.
- ☑ Ensure child car seats are used in other cars for your child.
- ☑ Tricycle and wheeled toys should only be ridden under supervision.
- ☑ Teach your child to get in and out of the car on the footpath side.
- ☑ Teach your child not to leave your house without an adult.
- ☑ Hold your child's hand when crossing and stepping on to the road.
- ☑ Keep your hot water temperature at 55°C.
- ☑ Put fireguards around fires and radiant heaters.
- ☑ Use close fitting children's night clothes.
- ☑ Keep medicines, detergents, cleaning agents and other poisons in high cupboards with safety locks.

- ✓ Buy medicines, detergents, cleaning agents and other poisons with child resistant closures/packaging
- ✓ Tools and garden poisons should be kept in a locked cupboard or shed.
- ✓ Sharp knives and scissors should be kept out of reach or in a drawer with a safety catch.
- ✓ Place safety glass, wooden bars or safety film across all glass at low levels.
- ✓ Secure safety catches on upper floor windows.
- ✓ Fence outdoor play areas.
- ✓ Ensure that the garage, driveway and work areas are not accessible.
- ✓ Give written safety instructions including your contact number to a responsible babysitter.
- ✓ Check how safe your child minder's home is.

Play materials

Cheap materials, most of which you'll have in your home, have been used in nearly all the activities in this book. Some items can be used in lots of different ways, so you won't have to go out and buy a lot of things to clutter your cupboards and shelves. The most expensive toys are not always the best toys, and because they're expensive doesn't mean that your child will prefer them.

Household items to save:

- Empty plastic bottles that have not contained poisonous or harmful substances.
- Large bottle caps, egg boxes, plastic containers.
- Cardboard boxes of all sizes.
- Aluminium foil and foil dishes.
- Old magazines, newspapers and junk mail.
- Kitchen towel tubes.
- String and wool.
- Paper, corks.
- Material scraps, cotton reels, wooden pegs.

Environmental items to collect:

- Shells, dried leaves, acorns, pinecones.

Note:
Pages 17 to 28 include instructions and recipes for play materials that have been suggested in some of the play@home preschool activities.

How to make a pom-pom

- To make a pom-pom, first cut two circles out of a piece of cardboard, and then cut the centre out of each circle. (see diagram 1)

- Place the two circles together, one on top of the other.

- Thread a double length of wool through the hole and over the edges (see diagram 2), binding firmly over the loose ends of the wool.

- Continue until the cardboard circles are completely covered.

Note:
Do not fill up the centre hole entirely, or the circles will be difficult to remove.

- Cut the wool round the outer edge, inserting the point of your scissors between the circles. (see diagram 3)

- Ease the circles slightly apart, and tie a length of wool very tightly between them. (see diagram 4)

- Pull off the cardboard circles, and trim off any uneven ends from the pom-pom.

- The finished pom-pom (see diagram 5).

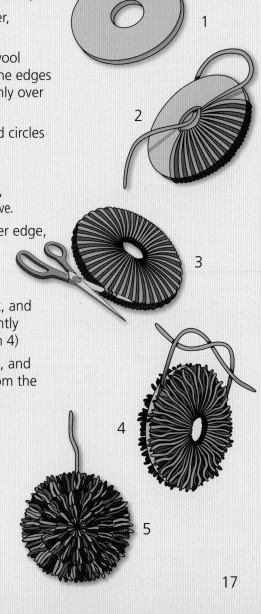

How to make a bean bag

- Cut out two pieces of fabric approximately 14 cm x 20 cm.

- Place the right sides of the fabric together and sew around the edges with a 1.5 cm seam, leaving a 5 cm opening along one side.

- Turn the fabric through the hole so that the seam is on the inside and iron it.

- Sew around the bag as close to the edge as possible, still leaving the 5 cm opening.

- Fill it with approximately two cups of uncooked rice, and then close the opening with two rows of stitching. (Dried peas, beans, lentils or sand can be used instead).

Bean bags can be thrown, balanced on your head or slid along the floor.

0

5 cm

10 cm

14 cm

Homemade glue recipes

1. Mix flour and water together until you get the consistency you want.

2. 1 cup water
   1 heaped teaspoon flour

- Mix the flour to a paste with a little water, then add the rest of the water and boil the mixture for a few minutes.

  Cool in a covered container.

Here are two different recipes for you to choose from:

Playdough (uncooked)

- 1 1/4 cup flour
- 1/2 cup salt
- 1/2 cup water

Combine the flour and salt, and slowly mix in the water. Work the mixture into a smooth dough with your fingers.

Playdough (cooked)

- 2 cups plain flour
- 1 cup salt
- 2 teaspoons cream of tartar
- 1 tablespoon cooking oil
- 2 cups cold water
- a few drops of food colouring, depending on the colour you want.

Place all ingredients except water and food colouring into a large bowl. Fill cup with water, add food colouring, gradually add to ingredients in the bowl, mixing well, then add second cup of water in the same way. Give a good whisk.

This mixture can be cooked in two ways:

Pan

- Pour the mixture into a large saucepan and cook over a low heat, stirring often with a strong metal spoon to prevent sticking on the bottom and to help even cooking.

- When the mixture has cooked and formed into a solid ball, remove from the heat. *Tip mixture on to a work surface, allow to cool slightly, then knead like bread dough for around two minutes. The dough is now ready to use. Store in an airtight container in the fridge. It should keep for a few weeks.

Microwave

- Place bowl of whisked ingredients into the microwave (remember to remove metal spoon or whisk), and cook on full power for around two minutes. Carefully remove from microwave and stir. Return to the microwave for one minute (approx), then repeat stirring and cooking until dough appears cooked. Make sure there is no uncooked dough but be careful not to over cook. Proceed as from *pan cooking method.

Variations

- To make your playdough a bit more interesting or to change the texture, add macaroni, glitter, oatmeal, colourings or scented flavourings.

Homemade paint recipes

Here are three different recipes for you to choose from:

1. Beat together soap flakes and warm water to make a mixture that looks like whipped potatoes. Add food colouring of your choice.

2. 1 cup cornflour
   1 cup soap flake
   1 litre boiling water
   food colouring
   Dissolve the cornflour in a little cold water. Slowly add the boiling water and boil until thick. Take it off the heat and beat in the soap flakes. Add food colouring.

3. 1 cup flour
   3 cups boiling water
   1 cup cold water
   food colouring
   1/4 teaspoon dishwashing detergent
   Combine the flour, detergent and cold water, stirring until it is smooth. Gradually pour the mixture into the boiling water and bring it to the boil, stirring constantly. Add food colouring and let it cool.

Note
These recipes can be used for either finger painting or brush painting. Store the paint in airtight containers. The paints made with soap flakes are easier to wash off clothes and surfaces.

Homemade bubbles recipes

Here are three different recipes for you to choose from:

1. Bubbles

   Mix together:
   18 fl oz water
   2 fl oz washing-up liquid
   4 teaspoons sugar

2. Longer lasting bubbles
   Mix together: 6 fl oz water
   2 fl oz washing-up liquid
   2 fl oz glycerine
   1 tablespoon sugar

3. Frothy bubbles
   For frothy bubbles mix liquid detergent and water,
   or bubble bath and water in a small bowl. Blow bubbles
   through a straw in the bowl. For coloured bubbles add
   some food colouring.

Remember – Do not let your child swallow the bubbles.

Hoola hoops

- Make your own hoola hoops. Join the two ends of a piece of old garden hose using a plug of wood. Secure the ends with some heavy duty tape or staples. Paint them with bright coloured, non-toxic paint or wind strips of coloured fabric around them and glue the fabric in place.

- Plait long strips of wool or other materials and join the two ends to make a loop. Thread some wire through the hoop to help keep its shape.

- In place of hoops draw a circle on a large piece of paper and place it on the floor or draw circles on the concrete with some coloured chalk. Make circles on the ground using a piece of wool or string.

- Plastic hoola hoops can be bought in most toy shops.

Markers

- Make your own marker cones by saving your plastic bottles and painting them with bright coloured non-toxic paint. Put a few stones, some dirt, water or sand in the bottom of the bottles so they don't fall over.

- Other items that can be used instead of marker cones are cereal boxes, bricks, blocks of wood, or large stones. A variety of markers such as books, toys and upside down bowls can be used.

- Plastic marker cones can be bought in most toy shops.

Homemade musical instruments

Drums

- Upside down saucepan and wooden spoon.
- Cardboard box and paper towel tube.

Shakers

- Rice in plastic bottle.
- Sand sealed in a small box.
- Rice sealed in yoghurt tubs.

Cymbals

- Two saucepan lids with knobs.

Tambourines

- Two disposable plastic plates, taped together, with uncooked rice between them.
- Two tinfoil dishes, taped together, with small stones, rice or dried beans between them.

Scrapers

- Sandpaper rubbed on a hollow cardboard box.
- Corrugated cardboard and a wooden spoon.

Comb tunes

- Run finger along the teeth of a comb.
- Wrap greaseproof paper around a comb leaving both ends open and blow or hum in one end.

Rattles

- Stones, rice or dried beans in an empty plastic bottle.
- Coins in a plastic money box.

Bells

- Glass containers or jam jars of different sizes filled with water at varying levels, and use a pencil or wooden peg as a striker. (Supervise this activity)

Rewards

Rewarding children for their efforts boosts their self-confidence and self-esteem. They respond well to praise and positive reassurance for trying. Rewards can be given to children after a game, or a Fun Session, to show you've noticed their efforts to try their best, to share and to take turns. If rewards are given, it is important that every child receives one. They do not need to be expensive, and avoid sweets as a reward.

Examples of rewards you may like to give:

- stickers
- stamp on each hand
- large star or a ribbon taped to their shirt
- homemade crown for each to wear home
- pet rock (small stone with a face painted on it)
- homemade playdough (see page 20).

Lucky dip

Fill a bucket with wood shavings or sand and hide a selection of little gifts (one for each child) in it.

Let the children take turns at digging into the bucket and pulling out a reward.

Musical treat bag

Ask the children to sit in a circle. Place small gifts (one for each child) in a bag and put on some music. Ask the children to pass the bag around the circle until the music stops. Ask whoever is holding the bag to take out one gift. Start the music again and repeat until each child has a gift.

Alternative – Let them take home something they have made such as a musical instrument (see page 25–26) or a picture of something they have drawn.

List of activities

Follow the leader

Instructions

- Ask your child and her friends to line up behind you.
- Have the children follow you, doing the same actions and movements as you.
- Lead the line around a course, walking forwards, backwards, side ways and zig-zag.
- Walk on tip toes, on heels, low, tall, big steps, small steps, feet close together and feet wide apart.
- Speed up and slow down.

Variations

- Have the children link hands as they follow the leader.
- Include arm movements such as swinging and circling the arms.
- Take them through an obstacle course (see page 118).
- Let the children take turns at being the leader.
- Continue to follow the leader but walk together as a group rather than in a line.
- Play follow the leader in pairs, taking turns at being the leader.
- Play 'Simon Says' where the children are facing you and they copy what you are doing.

Precautions

- Allow your child to develop her own interpretation of movement and actions and praise all efforts.

- Make sure her movement is not limited by tight clothing.

Suggested rhymes – One man went to mow page 144
 Ten in the bed page 149

 **benefits**

- **Physical – Developing movement skills, flexibility, balance and coordination.**
- **Other – Observing and copying movement Learning through group interaction and cooperation. Developing listening skills.**

Animals in the zoo

Instructions

- Join in a game with your child and his friends pretending to move like some of the animals in the zoo. Show how the animals move or visit the zoo so they can watch the animals.

- Encourage them to:
  - walk like an elephant swinging its trunk
  - scratch like a monkey
  - jump like a kangaroo
  - wash your paws like a lion
  - move like a crocodile
  - yawn like a hippopotamus
  - reach for leaves in a tree like a giraffe
  - walk on all fours like a bear
  - fly like a bird from branch to branch

- Let the children take turns at naming the animal.

- Let the children make animal sounds.

- Let the children draw their animals if they want to.

Variations

- Visit a farm together and pretend to be farm animals such as a cow, horse, sheep, rabbit, duck, chicken.

- Go on a nature walk and copy birds, ants and spiders.

- Reach up high like a tree and sway in the breeze like a flower.

- Take a trip to the beach and copy seagulls, crabs, fish, a dog digging in the sand, rubbing on sunscreen, and someone licking an ice-cream.

- Name different vehicles for the children to pretend to be: train, row boat, car, bus, truck, crane, plane.

Precautions

- Allow your child to develop his own interpretation of movement and actions rather than trying to make him see things the way you do.

- Make sure his movement is not limited by tight clothing.

Suggested rhymes – Hey diddle diddle page 136
Little Bo Peep page 141
Five little monkeys page 134
Baa baa black sheep page 132
Little boy blue page 142

 **benefits**

- Physical – Developing movement skills, flexibility, balance and coordination.

- Other – Observing and copying different movement patterns. Developing pretend play and learning to interact with others.

Walk tall

Instructions

- Help your child to balance a bean bag (see page 18) or small folded towel on his head.

- Practise walking around the room together balancing your bean bags or towels on your heads. Try not to let them fall.

- Sit down on a chair while still balancing your bean bags or towels on your heads, and stand up again.

Variations

- Have other children join in.

- Balance bean bags on their heads – nod and catch the bean bag in their hands.

- Try balancing different objects on their heads such as a book, newspaper, soft toy or plastic bowl.

- Ask the children to balance the object on the palm of their hands and the backs of their hands, first one hand and then the other.

- Balance objects on one shoulder, then the other shoulder and then an object on both shoulders at the same time.

- Have the children bend forward and then put an object on each of their backs. Ask them to walk around trying not to let the object fall off.

- Balance a bean bag on the upper part of one foot whilst trying to balance on the other leg.

Precautions

- Make sure there is plenty of clear space to play this game.
- Avoid extending this activity time to the stage where you or the children are not enjoying it.

Suggested rhyme – Head, shoulders, knees and toes page 135

benefits

- Physical – Developing balance, coordination and awareness of posture. Increasing awareness of body parts.
- Other – Learning by example. Experimenting with her centre of gravity and having fun. Learning left and right.

Board walk

Instructions

- Balance a board on two low boxes; one box at each end of the board.

- Encourage your child to walk to the end of the board, bend his knees and jump into an imaginary swimming pool and walk around and do it again.

- While he is walking the board he may need you to hold his hand to maintain his balance or he may balance by holding his arms out sideways.

Variations

- Narrow the width of the board to make it harder, and then try using a ladder instead of a board.

- Raise the height of the board to make it harder and then try raising one end more than the other.

- Ask him to walk the board with his hands out sideways, then at his sides, on his head and behind his back.

- Place obstacles on the board such as bean bags (see page 18) and ask him to step over and between them.

- Help him to learn to walk along the board backwards and then sideways.

- Add these activities to an obstacle course (see page 118).

Precautions

- The safest way to avoid climbing accidents is to teach him how to climb up and then climb down backwards. Supervise his first attempts at the activity.

- Make sure that he will land on a soft surface if he falls.

- Do not place the board too high.

Suggested rhymes – Humpty Dumpty page 137
Slip one and two page 147

benefits

- Physical – Developing balance and coordination.
- Other – Experimenting with height and gravity. Developing pretend play.

Marching soldiers

Instructions

- Use some rhythmic music or make your own rhythm by clapping or beating a drum (see page 25).

- Have your child move around the room stepping to the beat.

- Ask her to be a soldier marching with her back straight and her head held high.

- Once she has established a rhythmic pattern ask her to swing her arms at her sides as she marches.

- Teach her to take a right turn, left turn and about face.

Variations

- Sing a marching song together to do the activity, for example Grand old Duke of York.

- Have her friends join in to make a marching team, and each have a turn at leading and drumming the beat.

- Have her clap her hands on every fourth beat: 1, 2, 3 clap. Clap hands in front, above her head, behind her back.

- Go on a marching expedition: march on concrete, gravel, sand, grass and tarmac. March down an alleyway to make your steps echo. March along a crack in the footpath and along the edge of the kerb. March on tip toes, on heels, with legs wide apart and with legs close together.

- Take your child to watch a marching team or army drill.

Precaution

- Don't laugh at your child's attempts at rhythmic movement as she may become self-conscious.

Suggested rhymes – Ten little soldiers page 150
Grand old Duke of York page 135

 **benefits**

- Physical – Improving balance, left-right coordination and posture.
- Other – Developing a sense of rhythm, learning by observation and having fun. Encouraging creativity and imagination. Learning left and right.

Footprints

Instructions

- Provide your child with some paint (see recipe page 22) and a large piece of paper. Pour some paint into a shallow dish so that he can stand in the paint and then walk across the paper to make footprints.

- When the paint is dry, cut the footprints out and place them on the floor in sequence.

- Practise walking on the footprints placing the correct feet on matching prints. Count each step as you go.

- Vary the spaces between footprints.

Variations

- Make footprints along a large strip of old wallpaper by tracing around his feet.

- Make each print a different colour and encourage him to name the colour of each print as he steps on it.

- Number the footprints and then place them along the floor leading into the bathroom so that he counts each step he takes every time he goes to wash his hands.

- On a large piece of paper trace feet and handprints and then ask your child and his friends to match up one foot with a matching print, then the second foot, and then each hand. Encourage them to help each other to find the matching prints.

- Walk along a footpath and ask your child to try not to walk on any cracks.

Precautions

- If he becomes frustrated and has difficulty with the game leave it and let him go back to it when he's ready.

- Praise all attempts at the activity whether he is successful or not.

Suggested rhyme – One two buckle my shoe page 144

 **benefits**

- Physical – Developing balance, coordination and movement skills.
- Other – Learning by watching and copying. Developing body awareness and exploring new capabilities. Learning to count and naming colours.

Statues

Instructions

- Pretend to be a statue and ask your child to copy the way you are standing.

- Change your position to be a different statue and let her copy you again.

- Take turns at being the statue, copying each other's poses.

- Invite her friends to join in the game encouraging everyone to take turns at being the leader.

Variations

- Play some music for everyone to dance to. Tell them to 'freeze' in whatever position they're in when the music stops. Repeat this several times.

- Name shapes and objects and ask the children to be like one, such as a tree, ball, circle, chair, teapot or bridge.

- Go window shopping in town together and encourage your child to pose like the models in the clothes shop windows.

- Look at books together and try to copy the different poses of characters in the books.

Precaution

- Allow her to make poses in her own way and don't laugh at her attempts or she may feel self-conscious and refuse to play. Give plenty of praise for all her efforts.

Suggested rhymes – I'm a little teapot page 140
One two three a-leerie page 145

benefits

- Physical – Developing balance, coordination and flexibility.
- Other – Learning through watching and copying others. Developing body awareness.

Stepping stones

Instructions

- Cut out twelve shapes from an old newspaper or a roll of wallpaper to make stepping stones that are large enough for two feet to step on.

- Number the shapes from 1–12 so he can learn to read them easily.

- Place them on the floor in a circle.

- Have your child pretend that he has his new shoes on and if he steps between the stones he'll get covered in mud.

- Step from stone to stone in one direction, speaking out each number as he steps. Change direction.

Variations

- Vary the space between the stones so that he has to take very small steps and very big steps.

- Lay hoola hoops (see page 24) on the grass and step, jump or run from hoop to hoop.

- Use bricks, paving stones or blocks of wood as stepping stones.

- Set up an obstacle course (see page 118) that involves stepping from object to object and see if he can do it without touching the ground/floor.

- Encourage the use of words: to, from, over, around, between and so on.

Precautions

- If he becomes frustrated and has difficulty with the game try teaching it without the numbers until he understands, or leave it and let him go back to it when he is ready.

- Make sure the bricks and blocks of wood are sturdy and are unlikely to slide from under his feet.

 **benefits**

- **Physical – Developing balance, foot/eye coordination and movement skills.**

- **Other – Learning by watching and copying. Exploring new capabilities. Using imagination and learning to count.**

Horse and cart

Instructions

- Find a large cardboard box and help your child decorate it with wheels and colours so it looks like a cart.
- Attach a loop of string or skipping rope to the box as a harness.
- Have your child pretend to be the horse and pull the cart by putting the harness around his waist.
- This can be a useful game when tidying up because he can put all his toys into the cart and take them to his room.

Variations

- Vary the weight of the cart by putting heavier items in it.
- Encourage him to help in the garden by collecting all the leaves or weeds in the cart and then taking them and putting them on the compost heap.
- Develop a course around the garden for the horse and cart to follow, set up red, yellow and green traffic lights, and encourage him to pretend to go shopping.
- Have him drive the cart very slowly around the course and then quickly; galloping and then trotting.

Precautions

- Supervise your child at all times to make sure the harness stays around his waist.

- Children see things differently from adults so give him the chance to change things to suit his own play.

- Make sure that all fences and gates are secure so he does not come to any harm.

- Be patient. Sometimes having a 'helper' means that it takes twice as long to get things done.

Suggested rhymes – Yankee doodle page 155
Bell horses page 133
Horsey horsey page 137
Ride a cock horse page 146

benefits

- Physical – Developing balance, coordination and exercising many different muscles.
- Other – Using his imagination. Developing a sense of achievement, learning by observation. Establishing routines.

Streamers

Instructions

- Attach a tissue or piece of crepe paper to your child's wrists and ankles.

- Encourage her to stretch out her arms and pretend to be a bird, flapping her arms so that the streamers follow her arm movements.

- Then encourage her to run around the garden flapping her wings.

Variations

- Play this game on a windy day to get more movement with the streamers.

- Encourage her to walk backwards and sideways, to march and to jump.

- Have her lie on her back and make patterns in the air with the streamers on her ankles.

- Attach a streamer to her back and pretend it is a tail. Chase her and try to stand on her tail, and then let her chase yours, or a playmate's tail.

- Hold a streamer in each hand and make patterns and shapes in the air, or do this same activity with shoelaces or string in a bath tub.

Precautions

- Your child may prefer to make up her own game rather than take part in any structured play. Allow her the opportunity to do this.

- When playing the tail game ensure that you put her tail on her back soon after it comes off because she is likely to have become very attached to it.

- Never leave your child alone in the bath.

Suggested rhyme – Two little dicky birds page 154

 **benefits**

- Physical – Developing balance, coordination, flexibility and movement skills.
- Other – Observing, experimenting, interacting and thinking with others. Learning about air flow.

Movement to music

Instructions

- Ask your child and her friends to hold hands in a circle and dance round singing:
  'Here we go round the mulberry bush,
  the mulberry bush, the mulberry bush.
  Here we go round the mulberry bush
  on a cold and frosty morning.'

- Then ask them to stop dancing, stop holding hands, and follow your movements while you pretend to brush your hair, singing:
  'This is the way we brush our hair,
  brush our hair, brush our hair.
  This is the way we brush our hair
  on a cold and frosty morning.'

- Then all join hands and dance in a circle singing the first verse again. Repeat the song, changing the second verse each time, for example 'This is the way we clean our teeth', 'wash our hands', 'sweep the floor', 'paint the walls'.

Precaution

- Your child may not remember all the words or movements so allow her to interpret the songs in her own way with plenty of praise from you.

benefits

- Physical – Developing balance, flexibility and coordination. Coordinating movement with words.

- Other – Developing a sense of rhythm. Learning through observation and associating words with actions.

Hide and seek

Instructions

- Play hide and seek inside or within a play area outside.
- Show your child some hiding places, then close your eyes and count to ten slowly.
- Go and look for him.
- Take turns at hiding.

Variations

- Invite some of his friends to play. Help one of the children to hide his eyes and then count to ten with him. Then let him go and search for the others. Give everyone a turn.

- Play hide and seek with a teddy bear or some other toy in the lounge or bedroom. While your child is not looking place the bear somewhere in the room with a leg or arm visible so that your child can see it. Ask him to find it. Take turns at hiding the bear. When he knows most of the hiding places, hide the whole bear so that he can't see it.

- Play hide and seek among trees in a wood, or trees in a park.

Precautions

- Start this game very simply by letting your child see where you are hiding yourself or an object until he begins to understand the game.

- Don't give him a fright, or he may lose interest.

- Choose a play area free from dangerous obstacles.

- Teach your child not to hide outside the play area, in the clothes dryer, fridge, oven, under vehicles or machinery.

Suggested rhymes – Little Miss Moffat page 142
  Tommy thumb page 152
  I hide my hands page 140
  Wiggle your fingers page 155

benefits

- **Physical – Developing movement skills, coordination and an awareness of body size.**
- **Other – Encouraging him to think and develop memory skills. Learning about size in relation to shape and practising counting.**

Tunnelling

Instructions

- Make a tunnel by lying a large blanket over some chairs or over the washing line.

- Encourage your child and her friends to pretend they're going on an expedition to discover what is at the end of the tunnel.

- Give them a hat or bike helmet to wear, a real or imaginary torch and a snack.

- Encourage them to take turns at being the expedition leader.

- Take your child on a trip to explore some caves or to a mining museum.

Variations

- Vary the height of the tunnel so that they can walk, crouch, creep and crawl through it, forwards, backwards and sideways.

- Have them carry something, such as a ball, as they walk, crouch, creep and crawl through.

- Split the children into pairs and cover one child's eyes with a hat or mask and then ask her partner to lead her slowly through the tunnel. Then change over so that each has a turn to be blindfolded.

- Have all the children hold hands and play 'follow the leader' through the tunnel. Encourage them to take turns at being the leader.

Precautions

- Your child may become frustrated and have difficulty with learning to take turns, don't force her to do this, but give her the time to learn.

- Teach her not to go into tunnels or caves without you, or to dig tunnels.

benefits

- Physical – Developing movement skills and an awareness of body size.

- Other – Learning by watching and copying others. Developing her imagination. Learning to take turns and interact with others.

Volley balloon

Instructions

- Set up two chairs facing back to back with a piece of string tied between them.

- Blow up a balloon and stand with it on the opposite side of the string from your child.

- Show her how to hit the balloon with both hands to make the balloon go over the string, and then encourage her to do the same.

- Volley the balloon back and forth trying not to let it touch the ground.

Variations

- Have some friends join in and add some more balloons.

- Vary the height of the string.

- Play tennis with the balloon, hitting it with one hand and then the other.

- Have her hit the balloon up in the air and keep it in the air by hitting it upwards every time it comes down.

- Teach her to hit the balloon with her head.

Precautions

- When playing outside ensure the area is well fenced, so that if a balloon blows away she won't come to any harm chasing it.

- After energetic play offer a drink of water. Ensure she doesn't get cold.

Suggested rhymes – See-saw Margery Daw page 147

benefits

- Physical – Developing hand/eye coordination and balance.
- Other – Having fun and learning to associate words with actions. Experimenting with weight, gravity and timing.

Football

Instructions

- Use a lightweight ball that is large enough for your child to kick easily.

- Put the ball on the ground and kick it towards your child.

- Ask her to stop the ball and then kick it back to you.

- Encourage her to use either foot.

- Have some of her friends join in by making a large circle and then kick the ball to each other so that the ball moves in one direction from child to child.

- Once everyone has had two or three turns, change the direction by asking the children to kick the ball to the person on the other side of them.

Variations

- When she has mastered kicking a stationary ball encourage your child to kick the ball while it is rolling. Start by kicking the ball so that it will roll past her slowly and ask her to walk up to it and kick it. Teach her how to keep a ball rolling by running behind it and kicking it each time she catches up to it.

- Take her to a football match.

- Show her how to drop kick a balloon and once she is able to do that well let her try it with a ball.

- Encourage her to kick a ball between two marker cones (see page 24) and into a box that is lying on its side.

Precautions

- Give plenty of praise with each attempt at kicking, even when she misses.

- Don't expect her to kick a ball that is too small, too large or too heavy and avoid competing with her.

- Ensure the play area is well-fenced so that she doesn't chase the ball onto the road.

benefits

- Physical – Developing eye/foot coordination and balance.
- Other – Learning through observation and exploring new capabilities. Learning new words.

Ten-pin bowling

Instructions

- Stand ten plastic bottles in a group on the floor (place a small amount of sand or rice in each bottle to weight them slightly).

- Hold a lightweight ball in both hands, bend down, swing the ball between your legs and then roll it along the ground towards the bottles to knock them over.

- Count, together with your child, how many bottles have been knocked over.

- Stand the bottles up again, have your child stand two metres away from them and roll the ball towards them.

- Repeat this several times giving plenty of praise with every attempt.

Variations

- Vary the distance between your child and the bottles to make the game more challenging.

- Have other children take turns with bowling.

- Give him a smaller ball that he can easily hold in one hand and encourage him to throw it at the bottles, first under arm and then over arm, using either hand.

- Place two marker cones (see page 24) a metre apart on the ground and let your child take turns at bowling the large ball and then the small ball between the cones and into a box that is lying on its side. Vary the distance he stands from the cones.

- Take him to see a game of lawn bowls or visit a ten-pin bowling alley.

Precautions

- Do not use plastic bottles that have contained poisonous or harmful substances in case he tries to drink from them.

- Give plenty of praise with each attempt at bowling, even when he misses.

Suggested rhymes – Ten green bottles page 148
Ten fat sausages page 147

benefits

- Physical – Learning ball skills and developing balance and coordination.
- Other – Having fun and learning to interact and think about others. Learning to count.

Golf

Instructions

- Show your child how to hit a medium sized, lightweight ball around the garden with a kitchen towel tube or rolled up newspaper.

- Encourage him to hit the ball hard so that it travels a long way. (If his play area is small, have him hit it towards a concrete wall or garage door.)

- Lie some hoops (see page 24) on the ground two metres apart and encourage him to hit the ball into the middle of each hoop.

- Many children can play this game at the same time.

Variations

- Teach him how to play hockey by placing two cardboard boxes on their side, 4–5 metres apart, with the opening facing towards the middle. Show him how to use the kitchen towel tube to roll the ball along the ground towards a box and then hit the ball into the box. Repeat this in the other direction.

- Make a tennis racquet from a piece of stiff cardboard, or use a large plastic spade. Show your child how to hold it with two hands and then throw the lightweight ball towards the end of the 'racquet' and encourage him to hit it back to you. Repeat this several times and then let him throw it for you to hit.

- Let him watch people playing golf, hockey, tennis, cricket and table tennis.

- To play indoors use a balloon instead of a ball.

Precautions

- Give plenty of praise for all attempts and make it fun.
- Don't have unrealistically high expectations of your child. If he loses interest quickly, let him move on to another activity.

 **benefits**

- Physical – Developing hand/eye coordination, balance and movement skills.
- Other – Learning through observation and exploring new capabilities. Learning to associate words with actions.

Hoops

Instructions

- Scatter some hoola hoops (see page 24) on the ground at least three metres apart.

- Play some music that your child and his friends can dance to while they move around the hoops.

- Explain to them that when the music stops they are to run and stand in a hoop.

- After they've played this a few times begin to take one hoop away after each stop so that they have to share the hoops.

- When you get down to the last hoop run and jump in it with them. Huddle together and try to fit everyone in.

Variations

- Have the children dancing around the hoops as above but each time the music stops give them an instruction like: 'Put a hand in a hoop' or 'Put your elbows in a hoop'. Use as many body parts as you can think of, for example, the head, hand, nose, bottom, knee, tummy and finger.

- Use different coloured hoops and tell them to run to the red hoop, then hop to the green hoop, skip to the blue hoop, and so on.

- Use pieces of paper (coloured or numbered) instead of hoops.

- Place four hoops together in a square so that they are all touching and split the children into groups of three or four. Ask them to place a foot in a hoop, then the other foot in a different hoop, then a hand in another hoop and the other hand in the fourth hoop. This activity involves cooperation and often results in a lot of laughter.

Precautions

- Be sure his movement isn't limited by tight clothing.
- After energetic play give him a drink of water.

benefits

- Physical – General exercise and body part awareness.
- Other– Developing listening skills and practising following instructions. Learning colours and numbers and the names of parts of the body.

Fishing

Instructions

- Draw some fish on a piece of paper or on light cardboard, cut them out, and attach a paper clip to each one. Place them on a large piece of paper cut into the shape of a pond.

- Make a fishing rod using a kitchen towel tube with some wool attached to the end of it. Tie a magnet to the other end of the wool.

- Ask your child to stand on the edge of the 'pond' and try to catch a fish with her fishing rod.

- Make several rods and invite her friends to join in.

Variations

- Fill a basket with paper eggs, with paper clips attached, and let her try to lift all the eggs from the basket. Make each egg a different colour so that she learns each colour.

- Give her a long pencil, some plastic loops off the top of plastic milk bottles or cartons and a bowl. Ask her to pick up a loop on the end of the pencil and drop it in the bowl. Have her repeat this, counting each loop as she drops them in the bowl, until they're all in the bowl.

- Take her fishing or to watch other people catching fish.

Precautions

- Some children would prefer to be running, climbing or exploring rather than playing a concentration game, so don't be disappointed if she's not interested in this game for long – try again at a later stage.

- Never leave your child alone near water.

Suggested rhymes – One two three four five page 145
Row your boat page 146

benefits

- **Physical – Developing hand/eye coordination and hand skills.**
- **Other – Practising concentration, learning about colours and numbers and having fun.**

Sledge rides

Instructions

- After it rains, take your child and her friends for a walk in the countryside or a park.

- Take a sheet of polythene or plastic carrier bags with you and then find a long, gentle muddy slope.

- Let the children take turns at sitting on the bag as you pull them down the slope. Pull them faster each time.

- Encourage them to take turns at pulling each other down the slope on the bag.

Variations

- In the winter, visit a snowy slope and use sheets of polythene as sledges.

- Encourage the children to sit on a piece of cardboard and slide down the hill.

- On a sunny day lay a long sheet of polythene down on a gentle slope and spray some water on it so that the children can slide down it with their swimsuits on.

- Visit a park with slides of different sizes for the children to play on.

Precautions

- Wear old clothes and make sure movement is not limited by tight clothing. Do not worry too much about getting dirty – clothes and bodies can be washed!

- Let the children try these activities in their own time so they enjoy themselves and don't lose confidence.

 **benefits**

- Physical – Developing balance, coordination and movement skills. Exercising many different muscles. Parents exercising with their children.

- Other – Experiencing a sense of weightlessness and speed. Learning through imitation. Learning to associate words with actions. Having fun.

Climbing

Instructions

- Let your child practise climbing on different things.
- Let him climb onto chairs and off again by himself.
- Encourage climbing into and out of large cardboard boxes.
- Encourage him to practise going up and down stairs of different widths and steepness and in different ways.
- Show him how to climb a kitchen stool and a step ladder. Vary the angle of the ladder gradually so that it becomes steeper each time.
- Allow him to get in and out of the car himself.
- Give plenty of praise with every attempt.

Variations

- Climb hillsides together.
- Find as many different trees as possible for him to climb.
- Visit a rocky beach and help him to climb the rocks and boulders.
- Visit a farm and let him practise climbing up a farm gate and down the other side.
- Take your child and friends to a local playground where they can climb on ladders, see-saws, swings and other climbing frames.

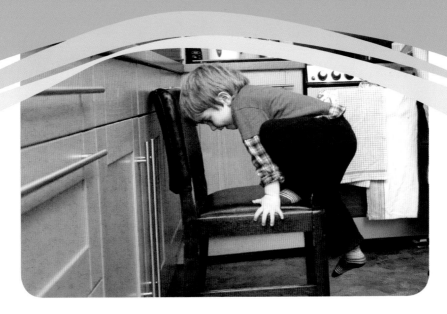

Precautions

- Supervise all climbing activities and make sure the climbing apparatus is sturdy and won't tip over.

- Be sure the surface underneath is soft to prevent injury.

- Encourage him to climb out of the car on the footpath side.

- Loose flapping clothing should not be worn, especially when tree climbing, to avoid accidents.

Suggested rhymes – Jack and Jill page 141
Incy wincy spider page 141

benefits

- **Physical – Developing coordination and flexibility skills. Exercising the whole body and having fun.**

- **Other – Learning about height, weight and gravity. Exploring new capabilities and learning by watching and copying.**

Opposites

Instructions

- Teach your child and her friends about the opposite meaning of words through play acting.

- Start with just two examples of opposites so they understand the meanings before moving onto new ones, and use gesturing to help the understanding.

- Begin with the words short and tall, by pointing out the difference between your child who is short and yourself, who is tall.

- Ask the children to pretend to be very tall by walking around with their arms stretched above their heads. Show them how they can make themselves taller by standing on a stool.

- Now ask them to be very short by crouching down as low as they can or encourage them to get down on their knees and move around.

- Look at pictures in books and magazines and point out short and tall people, buildings, and so on.

- Go for a walk in a park and point out short and tall trees.

Variations

- When looking at the words big and small, the children can be sent on a hunt around the garden to find a big and a small stone, leaf, twig, and so on.

- To learn about hot and cold, have the children pretend that they are going outside on cold day so they put on their hat, gloves and a coat. Then they pretend that it is a very hot day and they want to cool off so now they put on their swimsuits and a sun hat.

- Play 'over and under' in the bedroom – crawling over the bed and then under it.
- Think of other activities for teaching the meanings of opposites such as high and low, up and down, light and dark, open and closed, happy and sad.
- Always use gesturing to help your child understand.

Precaution

- Be patient, it takes longer for some children to remember the meanings of words than others.

Suggested rhyme – Two fat gentlemen page 153

 **benefits**

- **Physical – Practising a variety of body movements which relate to size, position, and so on.**
- **Other – Learning the meanings of words through imitation and association.**

Construction site

Instructions

- Save all your empty cardboard boxes for your child to build with.

- Find a spare corner in the house where he and his friends can build a house using empty cereal boxes, egg boxes, plastic containers and cardboard boxes.

- To make it more permanent, help them to tape the boxes together so they don't topple over.

- Encourage them to play imaginary games in their house.

Variations

- Show them how to line up boxes or chairs, one behind the other, to make a train or bus.

- Give them a cardboard box each to sit in and pretend they are cars, trucks, tractors or anything else.

- Encourage them to make a long tunnel by opening each end of their boxes and joining them together.

- See how high they can build a tower with cereal boxes before they topple over. Encourage them to count each box as it is stacked on. Do the same with building blocks.

- Show your child how to line up a row of cereal boxes or dominoes so that when one is knocked over it knocks down the others.

Precautions

- This activity needs team work – let the children manage this themselves.

- Encourage them to take turns and share.

benefits

- **Physical** – Practising balance, coordination flexibility and movement skills. Developing hand/eye coordination and body size awareness.
- **Other** – Experimenting with weight and gravity and learning to count. Developing creativity and imagination.

Bag of surprises

Instructions

- Fill a sack or pillow case with toys and utensils like a dustpan and brush, an egg whisk, a plastic spade, a pair of wellie boots, a hairbrush and a feather duster. Put in the same number of objects as there are children.

- Pass the sack around and ask each child to take out one object.

- Then ask them to pretend to use the object when you start the music.

- Move around and help each child to imagine that they are doing something with the object they chose, for example, using the spade to dig a hole, a farmer walking around the paddock in wellie boots or someone dusting the shelves.

- Collect up all the items and then pass the sack around again repeating the game two or three times so the children get a different object each time.

Variations

- Fill the sack with different hats for the children to play-act at being a farmer, nurse, firefighter, sailor and so on. If you do not have hats then cut pictures out of a magazine and use the pictures.

- Pass around a box with pictures of different animals and let the children pretend to be the animal on the card they choose while the music plays.

- Fill the bag with different musical instruments (see pages 25 and 26) that can be played along with some music.

Precautions

- There will be some objects that all the children will want to use so let them each take a turn with them.

- Allow them to use the objects in any way they wish and don't laugh at their attempts at imaginative play.

 **benefits**

- Physical – Developing balance, movement and coordination skills.
- Other – Developing creativity and imagination. Learning through pretend play.

Bubble fun

Instructions

- Make up some bubbles in a bowl (see page 23 for recipes).

- Make a loop with a pipe cleaner or wire coat hanger, or find a toy or utensil with a hole in that will make a good bubble blower.

- Take turns blowing bubbles and chase, poke, clap or stamp on them.

Variations

- Tie a piece of string between two chairs and blow the bubbles over and under it. Split a group of children into groups of three and have two hold hands with outstretched arms while the third blows bubbles over and under their arms (encourage them to take turns).

- Use the words: high, low, in front, behind, over, under, to and from.

- Blow the bubbles through a hoola hoop or a hoop made by another child clasping his hands in a circle above his head.

- Have your child lie on her back with her bare feet in the air and then blow bubbles towards her feet.

- Encourage your child to experiment with blowing bubbles from other positions such as between her legs or over her head.

Precautions

- Check the ingredients of the bubbles if you're buying them to avoid the risk of poisoning.
- Clean up spillages so no one slips over in the soap.

benefits

- Physical – Developing balance, movement and coordination.
- Other – Developing creativity and imagination. Learning through play, observation and learning to associate words with actions.

Gardening

Instructions

- Let your child watch you working in the garden: weeding, planting, pruning, fertilising and harvesting.

- Explain to her why you are doing what you are doing.

- Point out things of interest like a seedling pushing through the soil, new leaves and buds, a plant flowering. Watch their progress each day.

- Look together for insects in the garden and talk about what each one does. Let her watch a caterpillar, or other insect, eating a plant.

- Teach your child there is a time to be dirty and a time to be clean.

Variations

- Plant a variety of brightly coloured flowers. Name all the different parts of a flower (petal, stalk, leaf) and the colours of the flowers you have planted.

- Let your child have her own garden plot and help her to plant vegetables and fruit such as beans, carrots, lettuces and potatoes.

- Grow indoor plants such as bean sprouts and water cress.

Precautions

- Give her garden tools that are safe and are the right size for her.
- Children copy everything you do, so be patient and remember she is trying to be helpful.
- Make sure she is dressed in old clothes so you don't mind her being dirty.

Suggested rhymes – I had a little cherry stone page 138
Mary Mary quite contrary page 142
I hear thunder page 139

benefits

- **Physical – Developing hand skills, hand/eye coordination.**
- **Other – Learning about nature, how plants grow and why vegetables are good for you. Learning by observation. Learning new words.**

Swimming

Instructions

- Help your child learn to swim.

- Help him to begin to enjoy water by encouraging him to wash his own hair. Give him a shower so that he gets used to water on his face.

- When he's in the bath encourage him to lie on his stomach and kick his feet.

- Ask him to put his mouth on the surface of the water and blow bubbles. Once he has learnt to do this encourage him to put his whole face in the water and blow bubbles.

- Put some small objects on the bottom of the bath (before any soap is used) and ask him to open his eyes underwater and look for them. See how many he can pick up.

- Encourage him to lie on his back and float with your hands supporting him.

Variations

- Make short, frequent visits to a swimming pool with a shallow paddling pool to practise these activities in. Get into the pool with your child.

- Visit the beach and find a rock pool, or shallow water for him to swim and splash in.

- Enrol your child in water confidence classes at your local swimming pool.

Precautions

- Never leave your child alone with water because he can drown in a very small amount in a very short time.
- Protect him from hot water and the hot tap to prevent burns.
- Don't persist with any water activity he dislikes. It may cause him to lose confidence.
- If playing in a paddling pool in the garden in the summer, remember to apply water resistant sunscreen cream.

Suggested rhyme – Five little ducks page 133

 **benefits**

- Physical – Floating, kicking and splashing with resistance from the water. Practising deep breathing and exercising the whole body.
- Other – Developing water confidence and having fun. Learning new words. Learning water safety.

Exercise for everyone

Instructions

- Be a good example for your child, and his friends. Build at least 30 minutes of exercise into your daily routine. Let your child join in with you by copying or helping you with whatever you are doing.

- At the beginning of each day plan what you are going to do depending on the weather.

- On rainy days exercise activities at home may include doing the housework, dancing, exercising to music, joining in with an exercise class that is on television and so on.

- On dry days your home exercise activities may include gardening, hanging out washing, sweeping or raking up leaves, washing the car, tidying the garden or painting.

- Take notice of how active you and other family members are and try to do something energetic regularly.

Variations

- Go on family walks around the block, to the park, to the shops, to the beach and so on. Take this time to teach your child about his surroundings and what is happening around him.

- Take your child to watch people exercising and playing sports.

- Watch together how animals move and play.

Precaution

- You do not need to play sport to have an active lifestyle.
  Just be physically active daily.

Suggested rhyme – One finger, one thumb page 143

benefits

- Physical – Developing an active lifestyle by exercising regularly.
- Other – Learning through role modelling and watching and copying others.

Kitchen fun

Instructions

- Let your child help you in the kitchen.
- Begin to prepare meals early in the day so he can help to prepare food.
- Show him how to wash or peel potatoes, scrape the seeds out of a melon and wash lettuce leaves.
- Encourage him to count pieces of vegetables to make sure there are enough for everyone.
- Let him help you make meatballs or dip fish in breadcrumbs.
- Ask him to put together a salad with the ingredients you have prepared, he can cut the parsley with clean, round ended scissors.
- Encourage him to arrange raw vegetables in the shape of a face or a house on the plate.

Suggested rhymes – Hot cross buns page 137
Pat-a-cake page 145

Variations

- Encourage him to help you set the table; discussing which dishes and utensils you'll need for each meal and counting and placing them on the table correctly.
- Let him help you do some baking: sifting, measuring, mixing, rolling, kneading and decorating. Then he can watch to see how it changes when placed in a hot pan or the oven.

- Children need to learn how to clean up after working in the kitchen: helping to wash and dry the dishes, wiping down benches and putting things away can be very satisfying for them (and you!).

Precautions

- Be patient. Sometimes having a 'helper' means it takes twice as long to get things done.
- Always supervise children in the kitchen to avoid accidents.

benefits

- **Physical – Developing hand/eye coordination and practising hand skills.**
- **Other – Learning by observation and developing language. Discovering the concepts of weights and measures. Establishing routines and developing a sense of achievement.**

Waterworks

Instructions

- Fill a warm bath for your child to play in, with a non-slip mat in the bottom.

- Give him a variety of items to experiment with such as a plastic jar with a lid, a plastic jug, sieve, cork, rolled up tinfoil, sponge, egg box and a plastic ice-cream container.

- Encourage him to fill and empty containers and see how much water different items will hold.

- Ask him which items float and which sink, which are wet and which are dry, smooth and slippery, empty and full.

- Have him fill a squeeze bottle with water and then squirt a floating item to make it move.

Variations

- Let him fill a bowl or bucket for water play.

- Let him play with the garden hose, making patterns on the concrete, filling containers, watering the garden and so on.

- Find a rock pool at the beach or by a river and find items that can float and sink, and look for small creatures in the water.

- Help him wash his own dishes after meals, or bath his washable toys, and then dry them.

- Wash windows, walls, footpaths and fences together using rags, sponges or an old paintbrush and water.

Precautions

- Never leave your child alone with water because he can drown in a very small amount in a very short time.

- Protect him from hot water and the hot tap to prevent burns.

Suggested rhyme – Rub-a-dub-dub page 146

benefits

- **Physical – Developing hand/eye coordination, hand skills and balance.**
- **Other – Discovering the concepts of size, weight and quantity. Learning by observation and learning word association.**

Travel fun

Instructions

- Put together a bag of small items for your child to play with while you're travelling somewhere.

- Include a variety of items such as a bottle opener, peg, ribbon, photo, small stuffed toy, empty matchbox, small car or cork.

- Ask her to put her hand in the bag and take out one item and tell you where it came from and what it is used for. Repeat this until all the items are removed from the bag and discussed.

- Now put everything back in the bag and take turns at taking out an item and making up a story about each one.

Variations

- A magnet and some paper clips are fun to play with. She can also see what else will stick to the magnet, such as buckles on her shoes, metal buttons and zips or the seat belt clasp.

- A toy with a suction cup attached to it can be stuck to the window and pulled off again.

- Give her a box of small stickers and a notebook to decorate.

- Provide her with a piece of cardboard with holes in it and a long shoelace to thread in and out of the holes.

- Sing songs or rhymes together.

Precaution

- When going out in the car always strap her into a safe car seat. Contact your local Health Centre for information about car seats.

Suggested rhymes – The wheels on the bus page 151
Two little chickens page 153

benefits

- **Physical – Developing hand skills and hand/eye coordination.**
- **Other – Using her imagination, experimenting with science and having fun. Developing concentration skills.**

Artwork

Instructions

- Take your child and his friends on a nature walk to a nearby park.

- Give them a small paper bag each and ask them to collect small objects and put them in the bag.

- Collect items such as different coloured leaves, twigs, flowers and bark from a tree.

- When you get home give the children a large sheet of cardboard or heavy paper each and some glue so they can make a picture by gluing the different items onto the cardboard.

- Give them extra materials such as coloured wool, different shaped pastas, scraps of material and magazine pictures to add to their picture.

Variations

- Show them how to make a collage by cutting pictures out of magazines and gluing them onto a large sheet of paper.

- Make a continuous picture with a long sheet of wallpaper. Give the children some paint (see recipe page 22) and let them do finger and foot painting. Give them utensils to paint with such as a paint brush, an old toothbrush, a length of wool (dipped in the paint and dragged across the paper) and a leaf (dipped and then pressed onto the paper).

- Show them how to trace around hands, feet, boxes, bowls and different shaped objects.

Precautions

- Use small scissors with rounded ends for safety. Guide and supervise him while he is learning to use them.

- Some children prefer to be climbing, running and exploring rather than sitting, so don't be disappointed if he's not interested in this game for long – try again later.

 **benefits**

- Physical – Developing hand/eye coordination and hand skills.
- Other – Using creativity and imagination. Learning through experimenting, watching and copying others.

ABC and 123

Instructions

- Cut a potato in half and then carve a shape in each half to make stamps.
- Give your child a large piece of paper and some paint (see page 22) to dip the stamps in.
- Encourage him to make patterns and shapes on the paper using the stamps (squares, circles, triangles).
- Show him how to make letters and numbers.

Variations

- Make stamps with numbers on them. Teach him to count by writing the numbers across the top of a piece of paper and have him match them with the right stamp. The same can be done with the alphabet.
- Make stamps for each letter in his name and teach him how to make his name using the stamps.
- Rubber stamps can be used in the same way with homemade paint or an ink pad.
- Cut out cardboard letters and numbers and paint them in a variety of bright colours. Name the colours as you use them.
- Use magnetic letters and numbers attached to the fridge.

Precautions

- This should be a fun time for your child, so ensure that the emphasis is on play rather than teaching.

- Your child will need old clothes and plenty of newspaper down while using paints.

Suggested rhymes – One potato, two potato page 144
Alphabet rhyme page 132

benefits

- **Physical – Developing hand/eye coordination and hand skills.**
- **Other – Learning by observation. Encouraging him to think and use his imagination. Learning to count and name colours.**

Let's draw

Instructions

- Let your child experiment with colours, textures and different materials.

- Provide her with plenty of paper to draw on and pens, crayons, pencils and felt tips to draw with.

- Show her how to draw lines, circles, squares and faces and then let her copy them or do her own drawing.

- Encourage her to draw very small things on small pieces of paper. Then provide her with a large sheet of paper to draw very big pictures.

- Fold paper to make booklets and draw on each page to make her own book.

Variations

- Provide her with paints (see page 22) to experiment with. Start with the three primary colours – red, yellow and blue – as well as black and white. Show her how to mix colours, teaching her the names of the colours as you go. Let her experiment with using different things to paint with such as a paintbrush, toothbrush, string, leaf or sponge.

- Encourage her to use a stick to draw in dirt or sand.

- Chalk can be used on a blackboard, concrete or paving stones.

Precautions

- Tell her what she is and isn't allowed to draw on.

- Praise all efforts and ask her to 'tell me about your drawing' rather than asking 'what is it?' because she may have been drawing patterns rather than a thing.

- Old clothes or an apron are advisable when using paints.

benefits

- **Physical – Developing hand skills and hand/eye coordination. Learning to relax.**
- **Other – Developing her imagination and creativity. Learning about colours and shapes. Learning by observation.**

Wrapping presents

Instructions

- Make believe you are having a birthday party and show your child how to wrap up some of his toys as gifts.
- Use newspaper or recycled wrapping paper and some tape.
- Encourage him to wrap up small items, large items, oddly shaped things and slippery ones.
- Then let him unwrap them all again or give them to someone to unwrap.
- Give plenty of praise for his efforts.

Variations

- In the kitchen, let him help you wrap up the food scraps and put them in the rubbish bin, or wrap potatoes in tinfoil ready to bake.
- Show him how to wrap a doll or teddy bear in a small blanket and tuck it into bed.
- Ask him to cut small shapes out of cardboard and wrap them in tinfoil to hang on a mobile, or on the Christmas tree.
- Let him draw pictures and put them into envelopes. Then he can pretend to post them, or really post them to his grandparents.

Precautions

- Don't laugh at his efforts at wrapping.
- Accept his work as complete rather than trying to fix it up, which may make him feel as if he didn't do well.

Suggested rhymes – Happy birthday page 135

I sent a letter page 140

benefits

- Physical – Developing hand/eye coordination and hand skills.
- Other – Developing creativity and imagination. Learning by watching and copying.

How things grow

Instructions

- Take every opportunity to teach your child how things grow.

- Each time you go to the supermarket explain to her how two of the products you see are grown, for example, apples and carrots.

- Talk about whether the produce is grown directly in the soil, on a plant, a vine or a tree.

- If possible let her see the produce being grown by planting it in the garden together and watching it grow.

Variations

- Take her to visit a market garden or garden centre to see how various foods are sown, planted, grown and harvested.

- Visit the library together and find books and pictures on a variety of fruit and vegetables and talk about how they are grown.

- Once you have run out of different types of fruit and vegetables to learn about, move on to other products in the supermarket such as meats, eggs, cereals, dairy products, sugars, jams and so on. Your child can then begin to learn about how foods are processed, packed and delivered to the supermarket. Include visits to libraries, farms and factories.

Precautions

- Let your child learn at her own pace, she will not remember everything you teach her all at once.

- Supervise your child in the garden as some berries are poisonous.

- All her questions will seem important to her, so don't laugh at questions you think are silly.

Suggested rhymes – I have a little garden page 139
I had a little nut tree page 138

 **benefits**

- Physical – Exercise while learning.
- Other – Developing knowledge about science and nature. Learning about how foods are grown.

Tell me a story

Instructions

- Read to your child regularly, encouraging a love of books.

- Teach her how to care for books.

- Teach her how to hold the book, know back from front, upside down and so on.

- Visit your local library often and choose books together.

- Point to the pictures in the books and relate them to the words you are reading. Point to show her reading from left to right.

- Ask your child to point to pictures that you name and describe them, for example, 'What does Sam have on his head? What colour is his shirt? How many balloons is he holding?'

- Give her the opportunity to read books and tell stories to you.

- Get her to guess what might happen next before the next page or at the end of the book.

Variations

- Relate stories you have read to everyday activities. For example, talk about Peter Rabbit while you're weeding the garden, and discuss what food rabbits eat. Or discuss Thomas the Tank Engine when you see a train and count how many carriages it is pulling.

- Encourage your child and her friends to make up their own stories and tell each other about them. Provide them with materials to make their own books using sheets of paper, crayons, magazine pictures, glue, photos and so on.

Precautions

- Don't force your child to sit and listen to a story at a time when she'd rather be doing other things – books should be fun.

- Avoid reading books that have scary stories or that encourage violence towards people or animals or that stereotype men's or women's roles.

benefits

- Physical – Using pictures to learn about movement.
- Other – Practising listening and memory skills. Developing an enjoyment of books and increasing her vocabulary.

Write your name

Instructions

- Once your child has learnt to recognise his name he will begin to realise that his name is made up of a series of letters.

- Children often show an interest in the first letter of their name, like 'H' for Harry. Show him how to write the capital 'H' and the small 'h' and then let him practise it.

- Look through a magazine together and pick out the letters 'H' and 'h' from many different words. Let him cut them out and stick them in a scrapbook.

- Let him use a highlighting pen to show his letter in a magazine or newspaper.

- You can do this with the other letters in his name.

Variations

- Encourage him to find the letters of his name in a magazine, let him cut out the letters and glue them on paper to spell his name.

- He may enjoy making his name with playdough, or when finger painting (see pages 20 and 22).

- Encourage him to recognise the other letters of the alphabet and have fun writing them. For example 'A' and 'a' for apple, 'B' and 'b' for ball, 'C' and 'c' for car and so on.

- Once he has learnt a letter and a word that begins with that letter, he may like to write the letter and then draw a picture. For example, he can write 'A' and 'a' and then draw an apple.

Precautions

- Don't worry too much about how your child holds a pencil, he needs to try out different ways until he finds which is most comfortable.

- Provide him with small scissors with rounded ends for safety. Guide and supervise him while he is learning to use them.

- Old clothes or an apron are advisable when playing with glue and paints.

- Some children prefer to be climbing, running and exploring rather than sitting, so don't be disappointed if he's not interested in playing this game for long – try again at a later stage.

 # benefits

- **Physical – Developing hand skills and hand/eye coordination.**
- **Other – Learning by observation.**

Who are you?

Instructions

- Teach your child his full name and address so that he has it memorised.

- Play games in which he can practise using his name and address.

- Collect the mail from the letterbox together and look at the names and addresses written on the envelopes. Then address some envelopes to him and make a letterbox for him.

- Familiarise him with his neighbourhood and show him your street name on the sign post and the number on your house.

Variations

- Role play him being lost in a department store and teach him to go up to a counter and tell the shop assistant he is lost and what his name is.

- Write his name on his lunch box and bag to take to nursery so that he learns to recognise them easily.

- Ask him to draw a picture of your house with a letterbox and the street sign, and then write the street name and house number in for him and at the top of the picture write his name, for example 'John Cameron's house'.

Precautions

- Teach him to stay where he is if he gets lost so that you can come back and find him.

- Take the opportunity to teach road safety when you're out walking.

 **benefits**

- **Physical – Exercising while learning. Developing hand/eye coordination.**

- **Other – Practising listening and memory skills. Developing an awareness of his surroundings and increasing his vocabulary.**

Listen now

Instructions

- Sit in the garden with your child and close your eyes, or put a mask over your eyes.

- Lie in bed with your eyes closed in the morning listening for sounds before getting up.

- Listen carefully to all the different sounds around you.

- See how many different sounds she can identify.

- Now introduce more sounds, while her eyes are still closed, such as crumpling a dry leaf, tossing pebbles onto concrete and picking grass.

- See if she can guess what these new sounds are.

- Let her have a turn at making sounds for you to guess.

Variations

- Go for walks together and identify many different sounds in various places such as the park, beach, railway station or in the city.

- Sit in the dark together, inside and outside, and listen for different sounds such as a door squeaking or a dog barking.

- After playing listening games ask your child to remember all the things she heard and then draw them, or tell friends and family about the sounds she heard.

- Teach your child and her friends poems and songs, encouraging them to listen to and memorise them, and then repeat them often while doing other activities.

Precautions

- Don't force your child to take part in this activity at a time when she'd rather be running, climbing or doing other things, but use it to help her wind down after energetic play or before bed.

- When playing this game avoid creating a fear of the dark.

Suggested rhymes – Twinkle twinkle little star page 152
Two little feet page 154

benefits

- **Physical – Relaxing and stretching her muscles and practising deep breathing.**
- **Other – Practising listening and memory skills. Developing an awareness of her surroundings and sharpening her senses.**

Let's pretend

Instructions

- Lie down on the grass under a tree with your child and his friends and listen to the birds chirping in the tree.

- Pretend to be cats curled up under a tree by asking the children to curl their bodies up like a sleeping cat. Then ask them to stretch like a cat, positioned on their hands and knees, arching their backs up and taking a deep breath in. Curl up again as you all let your breath out slowly. Repeat this two or three times.

- Next, staying on your knees, take a deep breath in as you stretch your arms towards the branches of the tree and try to reach a bird. Then breathe out as you all go down onto your hands and knees. Repeat this two or three times.

- Then tell the children that all the birds have flown away so they can curl up like cats and go back to sleep again.

Variations

- Pretend to be waves rolling your bodies gently to one side and then the other. Then get on your hands and knees and ask them to slowly walk their hands forward, away from their bodies as they take a deep breath in, pretending to be waves creeping up the beach. Breathe out slowly as you slide your hands back towards your knees. Repeat two or three times and then lie down and pretend you are floating on the sea.

- Pretend to be flowers that open their petals in the daytime; stretching your arms out wide as you breathe in, and then close them at night time; fold your arms around you as you breathe out. Repeat two or three times and then lie down and imagine the breeze blowing on the flowers.

Precaution

- Some children will not be able to visualise what you see be patient and allow them to develop their own images.

benefits

- **Physical – Practising deep breathing and stretching exercises. Learning to relax.**
- **Other – Developing the imagination and learning by imitation. Providing parents with a useful activity for winding down excited children and themselves.**

Parachute games

Instructions

- Make a parachute out of nylon material.
- Cut out wedge-shaped pieces of fabric and sew them together to form a circle.
- Leave a hole in the middle of the circle so that the parachute works.

Games using your parachute

- It is essential that parents, carers and family members join in these games to make it a more enjoyable time for your children.

1 Making waves

- Spread the parachute out and organise the group around the edge. Hold the parachute at waist height with both hands and shake it up and down vigorously and watch the waves that are formed. Make big waves and small waves.

2 Flatten the air bubbles

- Kneel down on the ground and make waves as above.
- Encourage the children to run around on top of the parachute and jump on the air bubbles as you make them. (This needs to be played on a soft surface such as grass or sand.)

3 Popcorn

- Spread the parachute out and organise the group around the edge, holding the parachute at waist height with both hands. Throw 6–10 small balls into the parachute and have the group pop them in the air. Encourage them to throw the balls to the outer edges so that they are bounced back in again. (The balls can be foam balls, rolled up tinfoil or pom-poms.)

4 Air balloon

- Spread the parachute out with all the adults around the outside. (Make sure the children are not holding on to the parachute because it may lift them off the ground.)

- Count 1-2-3 and lift the parachute above your heads. When it has gone as high as it will go, walk forward four steps and then back out as it comes down.

- Encourage the children to run under the parachute while it is in the air and then out again before it lands on the ground.

- Encourage them to stand under it and reach up high to touch it as it comes down. Then ask them to lie on their backs under the parachute with their feet in the air reaching up to the parachute as it comes down again.

5 Spaceship

- Spread the parachute out with all the adults around the outside. (Make sure the children are not holding on to the parachute because it may lift them off the ground.)

- Count 1-2-3 and lift the parachute above your heads and ask all the children to run under the parachute. Walk forward two steps, bring the parachute down behind your backs and sit on the edges, trapping the air. You all end up sitting under the parachute, making a spaceship.

- While in the spaceship have the children sit around the edges of the parachute and start rhythmical rocking movements. Rock the spaceship in different directions and back and forth.

- You may like to include songs.

6 Merry-go-round

- Spread the parachute out and organise the group around the edge. Hold onto the parachute with one hand and travel around in a circle – run, hop, leap, and then change direction.

- Hold it with two hands and, facing inwards, move around using a shuffle, side step, cross-over steps and so on. Move quickly and slowly.

- You may like to include music and songs.

7 Sliding

- This needs to be played on a shiny floor.

- Spread the parachute out and organise the group around the edge. Sit on the floor with your legs under the parachute, facing inwards, and hold onto the parachute with both hands.

- Count 1-2-3 and everyone pull hard on the parachute so that they slide under the parachute with all feet pointed towards the centre.

- Then move back by 'walking' on your bottoms to the place you started at.

- Repeat several times.

8 Tunnelling

- Spread the parachute out on the floor and encourage the children to crawl under it on their hands and knees from one side to the other, then stand up, run around the outside of the parachute and tunnel again. For variation, have them pick up a ball and take it through with them.

- Do not allow any children to walk or run on top of the parachute while others are underneath it.

9 Tug of war

- Divide the group into two sides. Each side pulls on the parachute as in a regular tug of war.

10 Cooling down

- To finish off an energetic activity session take turns lying under the parachute while the others create a fan by shaking the parachute.

Precautions

- Allow your children to join in the parachute games when they are ready so that they don't lose confidence.
- Make sure you have plenty of space to play parachute games to avoid accidents.

benefits

- Physical – Developing balance, movement skills, flexibility and coordination. Using many of the muscles in the body. Parents and family exercising with the children.
- Other – Learning about movement, space, gravity and air movement. Developing self confidence, interacting cooperatively with others and having fun. Learning through imitation and experimentation.

Obstacle courses

Instructions

- Moving around an obstacle course is an ideal way of helping your child to learn and practise a variety of skills, to develop concentration and imagination, and to have fun.

- It involves setting up a course, inside or outside, using obstacles or equipment which must be travelled over, under, around, through or along.

Obstacle course ideas

- Step, jump and run through hoops (see page 24) spread along the ground.
- Zig-zag around a row of marker cones (see page 24).
- Crawl through a cardboard box tunnel or a blanket tunnel (see page 54).
- Climb over, or crawl under, a table.
- Walk along a bench or board (see page 36).
- Climb up and walk along a row of chairs, and jump down.
- Climb over a gate or climbing frame.
- Walk along some stepping stones (see page 44).
- Jump over a piece of rope or a cushion.
- Step between a row of tyres.
- Crawl under, or step over, a series of low ropes.
- Run up and/or down a slope or some steps.
- Circle or zig-zag around a row of trees.

Variations

- Set up an obstacle course inside or outside depending on the space available, the weather and the number of children.

- When the children have got used to the course let them try to do it as quickly as possible, slowly, backwards and in the opposite direction.

- Give them a ball to carry around the course with them. Then have them do the course while holding the ball on their heads and then behind their backs. Let them balance a bean bag (see page 18) or a folded towel on their heads as they move around the course.

- Encourage the children to do the course in pairs or have them all hold hands and do the obstacle course without letting go.

Precautions

- Begin with a very simple course and then gradually make it harder.

- Allow the children to join in when they are ready.

- Allow the children to do the course in their own way.

- They may become frustrated and have difficulty learning to take turns. Be patient and give them time to learn.

- Supervise and help the children with activities they are attempting for the first time.

- If the children are likely to fall, play on a soft surface like rubber matting or bark.

- After energetic play offer the children a drink of water and make sure they don't get cold.

 # benefits

- Physical – Developing balance, coordination, flexibility and movement skills. Experimenting with a wide range of movement patterns and activities.
- Other – Developing confidence and independence. Learning through watching and copying. Learning to take turns and interact with others.

Fun sessions

A fun session is a structured activity session for children involving a variety of exercises and activities that are challenging, interesting and fun. The session includes a five minute warm up, a fifteen minute activity session and then a five minute cool down and stretching time. Fun sessions can be organised for any number of children and require very little equipment. Plan a fun session for any occasion, for example:

• birthday parties

• family gatherings

• play groups

• parents' day at nursery

Instructions

• Use the ideas in this play@home book to prepare your fun session, and plan the games before you start.

• Begin with one or two 'warm up' games which are simple and not too energetic. Let the children join in when they are ready. (Warm up for around five minutes.)

• When all the children have joined in and begun to enjoy themselves, move on to more energetic and challenging activities. (About 15 minutes.)

• End the session with one or two cool down and stretching activities. (5 minutes.)

• Make up your own games or visit the library for ideas and include them in your fun session.

Example of a fun session:

Warm up (5 mins)   Movement to music
Music that has actions to it such
as a bird dance or Mulberry bush

Activity (15 mins)   Obstacle course
Parachute games

Cool down (5 mins) Let's pretend

benefits

- Physical – Developing hand skills and coordination. Exercising many different muscles.
- Other – Discovering the concepts of size, shape, quantity and weight. Learning to observe and interact with others. Learning new words.

Other activities you can choose from the play@home programme:

Warm Ups	Bag of surprises
	Fishing
	Animals in the zoo
	Follow the leader
	Marching soldiers
	Ten pin bowling
Activities	Hoops
	Exercise for everyone
	Volley balloon
	Streamers
Cool Down	Statues
	Bubble fun
	Water works
	Let's draw
	Musical treat bag
	Massage

Precautions

- Praise each child for attempting the activities and joining in – there should be no winners or losers.

- Make the activities appropriate, achievable, safe and fun.

- Avoid extending the activity time to the stage where you or the children are not enjoying it.

- If the children are likely to fall, play on a soft surface like rubber matting or bark.

- Watch and help each child as they try an activity.

- If the activities are outside, use sunblock cream and hats to prevent sunburn, or put on warm clothing on cold, windy days.

- After the activities give the children water to drink and make sure they don't get cold.

- Give yourself a reward for organising and supervising a very valuable session.

benefits

- **Physical – Exercising the whole body and developing balance, coordination, movement skills and flexibility. Stretching, exercising and deep breathing. Parents exercising with their children.**

- **Other – Developing good habits and having fun. Learning through watching and copying. Learning to take turns. Beginning to understand about warming up the body, playing energetically, cooling down and stretching.**

Additional games

Sharks

In pairs, half of the children stand facing one another with hands joined in the air to make bridges. The other children are the 'fish'. On the command 'Swim, fish swim' the 'fish' swim around or under the bridges until they hear the call of 'sharks'. At this point the fish have to seek safety under the bridges but only one fish per bridge is allowed. Any fish who are out can then be bridges and bridges can become fish. Give all the children turns at being bridges and fish.

Beans

The children can dance to music. When the music stops the adult can call out a type of bean – the children then have to 'show' the bean:

jelly bean	• children shake and wobble
runner bean	• children run around
french bean	• children stand tall and thin
butter bean	• children curl up into a round shape
beans on toast	• children lie spread out on floor
jumping bean	• children jump around
broad bean	• children make wide shapes

Cat and mouse

Depending on the size of the group playing, choose two or more children to be cats. Give the rest of the children a tail by tucking a band in at the top of their shorts at the back. The cats have to catch as many tails as they can.

Magic carpet

A group of children sit on a 'magic carpet' and sing 'fly carpet fly'. The children can use their arms and pretend to fly. One child can be asked where he/she would like the carpet to land. On landing, the children get off the carpet and play at the chosen place, such as at the beach, at the zoo or at the play park.

The squeeze

This game can be played at the end to calm everyone down. The children sit in a circle holding hands. One person starts the squeeze by giving just one hand a squeeze. The next child then has to pass on the squeeze to the other hand until the squeeze goes right round the circle and back to the first person.

Child massage

- Give your child plenty of cuddles, loving touch and close contact every day.

- Make the most of opportunities to massage him when he's sitting quietly looking at books or toys, during bath time, at bedtime or any other time he needs calming and settling.

- Use cuddles and reassuring touch to make your child feel better about anxieties and fears and to help both of you to deal with frustration and tantrums.

- Let him give permission to be massaged or cuddled and to break contact when he chooses.

- Be aware of your child's likes and dislikes with loving touch and change your massage to suit him.

All children, including those with special needs, respond well to cuddles and loving touch. For children with special needs discuss this with your child's therapist.

Action songs

Alphabet rhyme

A, B, C, D, E, F, G

H, I, J, K,

L, M, N, O, P,

Q, R, S, T, U, V,

W, X, Y, Z.

Now I know my ABC

Next time won't you sing with me?

Baa baa black sheep

Baa baa black sheep

Have you any wool?

Yes sir, Yes sir, three bags full

One for the master and one for the dame

And one for the little boy who lives down the lane.

Bell horses

Bell horses, bell horses
What time of day?
One o'clock, two o'clock
Three and away.
Bell horses, bell horses
What time of day?
Two o'clock, three o'clock
Four and away.
Bell horses, bell horses
What time of day?
Five o'clock, six o'clock
Now time to play.

Five little ducks

Five little ducks went
swimming one day

Over the hills and far away
Mummy duck said 'quack
quack quack quack'

But only *four little ducks
came back

Repeat with *three, two, one

Last verse, last line –

And all the five little ducks
came back.

Five little monkeys

Five little monkeys walked
along the shore

One went a-sailing

Then there were four

Four little monkeys climbed
up a tree

One of them tumbled down

Then there were three

Three little monkeys found
a pot of glue

One got stuck in it

Then there were two

Two little monkeys found
a currant bun

One ran away with it

Then there was one

One little monkey cried
all afternoon

So they put him in an aeroplane

And sent him to the moon!

Grand old Duke of York

The grand old Duke of York

He had ten thousand men

He marched them up to the
top of the hill

And he marched them
down again.

When they were up they
were up

And when they were down
they were down

But when they were only half
way up

They were neither up nor down.

Happy birthday

Happy birthday to you

Happy birthday to you

Happy birthday, dear ....

Happy birthday to you.

Head, shoulders, knees and toes

Head, shoulders, knees
and toes, knees and toes

Head, shoulders, knees
and toes, knees and toes

And eyes and ears and
mouth and nose

Head, shoulders, knees
and toes, knees and toes.

Hey diddle diddle

Hey diddle diddle
The cat and the fiddle
The cow jumped over the moon
The little dog laughed
To see such fun
And the dish ran away with
the spoon.

Hokey cokey

You put your right hand in
You put your right hand out
You put your right hand in
And you shake it all about
You do the 'hokey cokey'
And you turn around
That's what it's all about
See!
Oh hokey, cokey, cokey
Oh hokey, cokey, cokey
Oh hokey, cokey, cokey
That's what it's all about
See!
Repeat with – left hand
right foot
left foot
right ear
left ear
whole self.

Horsey horsey

Horsey horsey don't you stop

Just let your feet go clippety clop

The tail goes swish and the wheels go round

Giddy-up we're homeward bound.

Hot cross buns

Hot cross buns

Hot cross buns

One a-penny, two a-penny

Hot cross buns.

Humpty Dumpty

Humpty Dumpty sat on a wall

Humpty Dumpty had a great fall

All the king's horses and all the king's men

Couldn't put Humpty together again.

I had a little cherry stone

I had a little cherry stone
And put it in the ground
And when next year I went
to look
A tiny shoot I found
The shoot grew upwards
day by day
And soon became a tree
I picked the rosy cherries then
And ate them for my tea.

I had a little nut tree

I had a little nut tree
Nothing would it bear
But a silver nutmeg
and a golden pear
The King of Spain's daughter
Came to visit me
And all because of
my little nut tree.

I have a little garden

I have a little garden
Where I like to go
And that is where
All the *red poppies grow
*Repeat with
blue bells
green grass
yellow buttercups.

I hear thunder

I hear thunder, I hear thunder
(drum feet on floor)
Hark don't you?
Hark don't you?
(Pretend to listen)
Pitter patter raindrops
(indicate rain with fingers)
Pitter patter raindrops
I'm wet through
(shake body)
So are you
(point to friend).

I hide my hands

I hide my hands
I shake my hands
I give a little clap
I clap my hands
I shake my hands
I hide them in my lap.

I sent a letter

I sent a letter to my love
To my love, to my love
I sent a letter to my love
And on the way I dropped it.

I'm a little teapot

I'm a little teapot
Short and stout
Here's my handle
Here's my spout
When the tea is ready
Hear me shout –
Tip me up and pour me out.

Incy wincy spider

Incy wincy spider
Climbed up the spout
Down came the rain
And washed the spider out
Out came the sunshine
Dried up all the rain
Incy wincy spider climbed
up the spout again.

Jack and Jill

Jack and Jill went up the hill
To fetch a pail of water
Jack fell down
And broke his crown
And Jill came tumbling after.

Little Bo-Peep

Little Bo-Peep,
has lost her sheep
And doesn't know
where to find them
Leave them alone and
they'll come home
Wagging their tails
behind them.

Little boy blue

Little boy blue come blow your horn

The sheep's in the meadow, the cow's in the corn

Where is the boy who looks after the sheep

He's under the haystack fast asleep.

Little Miss Moffat

Little Miss Moffat

Sat on a tuffet

Eating her curds and whey

There came a big spider

Who sat down beside her

And frightened Miss Moffat away.

Mary Mary quite contrary

Mary Mary quite contrary

How does your garden grow?

With silver bells and cockle shells

And pretty maids all in a row.

One finger, one thumb

One finger, one thumb,
keep moving.

One finger, one thumb,
keep moving.

One finger, one thumb,
keep moving.

We'll all be merry and bright.

One finger, one thumb, one
arm, one leg, keep moving.

Repeat twice...

We'll all be merry and bright.

One finger, one thumb, one arm,
one leg, one nod of the head,
keep moving.

Repeat twice...

We'll all be merry and bright.

One finger, one thumb, one
arm, one leg, one nod of the
head, stand up, sit down,
keep moving.

Repeat twice....

We'll all be merry and bright.

One finger, one thumb, one
arm, one leg, one nod of the
head, stand up, sit down, turn
round, keep moving.

Repeat twice....

We'll all be merry and bright.

143

One man went to mow

One man went to mow

Went to mow a meadow

One man and his dog

Went to mow a meadow.

Repeat using two, three etc,
up to ten.

One potato, two potato

One potato, two potato,
three potato, four

Five potato, six potato,
seven potato, more.

One two buckle my shoe

One two buckle my shoe

Three four shut the door

Five six pick up sticks

Seven eight lay them straight

Nine ten a big fat hen

Eleven twelve dig and delve

Thirteen fourteen maids
a-courting

Fifteen sixteen maids
in the kitchen

Seventeen eighteen maids
in waiting

Nineteen twenty
my plate's empty.

One two three a-leerie

One two three a-leerie
Four five six a-leerie
Seven eight nine a-leerie
Ten a-leerie, watch me.

One two three four five

One two three four five
Once I caught a fish alive
Six seven eight nine ten
Then I let it go again.
Why did you let it go?
Because it bit my finger so.
Which finger did it bite?
This little finger on my right.

Pat-a-cake

Pat-a-cake, pat-a-cake,
baker's man
Bake me a cake as fast
as you can
Pat it and prick it
And mark it with 'B'
Put it in the oven
for baby and me.

Ride a cock-horse

Ride a cock-horse to Banbury
Cross

To see a fine lady upon
a white horse

With rings on her fingers
and bells on her toes

She shall have music wherever
she goes.

Row your boat

Row, row, row your boat

Gently down the stream

Merrily, merrily, merrily, merrily

Life is but a dream.

Rub-a-dub-dub

Rub-a-dub-dub

Three men in a tub

And who do you think they be?

The butcher, the baker, the
candlestick maker

Turn them out knaves all three.

See-saw Margery Daw

See-saw Margery Daw
Johnny shall have a new master
He shall have but a penny a day
Because he can't work any faster.

Slip one and two

Slip one and two
Jump three and four
Turn around swiftly
And sit upon the floor
Clap one and two
Nod three and four
Jump up again
And be ready for more.

Ten fat sausages

Ten fat sausages sitting in a pan
One went 'pop' another went 'bang'
Eight fat sausages and so on.
No fat sausages sitting in a pan.

Ten green bottles

Ten green bottles hanging on the wall

Ten green bottles hanging on the wall

And if one green bottle should accidentally fall

There'd be nine green bottles hanging on the wall.

Repeat with nine, eight, seven, etc.

Ten in the bed

There were ten in the bed

And the little one said

Roll over! Roll over!

So they all rolled over

And one fell out...

There were nine in the bed,
and so on down to one.

There was one in the bed

And the little one said

Roll over! Roll over!

So he rolled right over
and fell right out

There were none in the bed

So no one said

Roll over! Roll over!

Ten little soldiers

(action rhyme for fingers)

Ten little soldiers stand up
straight

(Hold up both hands palm
outwards)

Ten little soldiers make a gate

(Reverse hands hold them
downwards)

Ten little soldiers make a ring

(Hold hands palms facing, little
fingers and thumbs touching)

Ten little soldiers bow
to the king

(Bend all fingers)

Ten little soldiers dance all day

(Wiggle all fingers)

Ten little soldiers hide away

(Hide fingers behind back).

The wheels on the bus

The wheels on the bus go round and round

Round and round, round and round

The wheels on the bus go round and round

All day long.

Repeat with horn... goes toot toot toot

wipers... go swish swish swish

people... go up and down

driver... goes broom broom broom

Three blind mice

Three blind mice, three blind mice

See how they run, see how they run

They all ran after the farmer's wife

Who cut off their tails with a carving knife

Did you ever see such a thing in your life

As three blind mice.

Tommy Thumb

Tommy Thumb, Tommy Thumb
Where are you?
Here I am, here I am
How do you do.
Repeat with:
Peter Pointer, Toby Tall, Ruby Ring, Baby Small, Fingers All.

Twinkle twinkle little star

Twinkle twinkle little star
How I wonder what you are
Up above the world so high
Like a diamond in the sky
Twinkle twinkle little star
How I wonder what you are.

Two fat gentlemen

(finger rhyme)

Two fat gentlemen
met in a lane

Bowed most politely,
bowed once again

How do you do?
How do you do?

How do you do again?

(Use thumbs)

Repeat with:

Two thin travellers met
in a lane.

(1st fingers)

Two tall ladies

(middle fingers)

Two little babies

(baby fingers).

Two little chickens

Two little chickens looking
for more

Along came another two
and that made four

Four little chickens were
in such a fix

Along came another two
and that made six

Six little chickens were
pecking at the gate

Along came another two
and that made eight

Eight little chickens
ran to Mother Hen

There they found another
two and that made ten.

Two little dicky birds

Two little dicky birds
Sitting on a wall
One named Peter, the other
named Paul
Fly away Peter
Fly away Paul
Come back Peter
Come back Paul.

Two little feet

Two little feet go tap tap tap
Two little hands go clap clap
clap
Two little eyes open wide
One little head wags from
side to side.

Wiggle your fingers

Wiggle your fingers
Wiggle your toes
Stand your soldiers
(fingers)
In two straight rows.
Hide your fingers
Hide your toes
No more soldiers
In two straight rows.

Yankee Doodle

Yankee Doodle came to town
Riding on a pony
He stuck a feather in his cap
And called it macaroni.

This programme has been developed to encourage all children to begin a life of healthy exercise and sport and to promote positive learning opportunities for all preschool children. They will continue to appreciate the benefits of play and activities as they move into school, developing new friendships, encouraged by you, their parents, as you continue to support them not only in what they do, but in what you do with them.

With thanks to Glenrothes Twins and Multiples Club and North Edinburgh Arts Centre for taking part in our photo shoots.

Picture credits